BOOK 3

Ruth Mis

G000230072

Superphonics

The simplest, fastest way to teach your child to read

Contents

Hodder Children's Books

a division of Hodder Headline

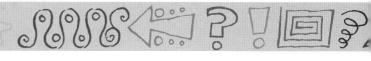

What is meant by the term 'phonics'?

Phonics is a highly effective way of teaching reading and spelling, based on the link between sounds and the way in which we write them down. A unit of sound is called a phoneme (*foe-neem*), and the written version of it is called a grapheme:

c / a / t   contains 3 graphemes and 3 phonemes

ch / a / t   contains 3 graphemes and 3 phonemes

f / l / a / t   contains 4 graphemes and 4 phonemes

Note: A phoneme may contain more than one letter. A letter has a name: *dee*
                    and a sound: *d (d)*

Letters are divided into 2 groups:
Vowels: *a e i o u*
Consonants: *b c d f g h j k l m n p q r s t v w x y*

How does *Superphonics* teach this?

There are 5 books in the series. The chart on the inside front cover shows which graphemes/ phonemes are taught in each book. Each book builds on the skills already learned, and there are plenty of opportunities for revision and practice.

Each book is divided into units, all of which are organised in the same way.

Each unit in this book and Books 2, 4 and 5 consists of 6 steps:

STEP 1 FIND THE RHYMING WORDS
The ability to rhyme is an important skill. If your child can read and spell *cat*, he or she will be able to read and spell *mat* – and so on.

STEP 2 FIND THE SOUNDS
Now your child is taught to hear the separate phonemes in a word: *c / a / t*. Most children need to be taught that each word is made up of individual sounds. In the game Phoneme Fingers, your child is taught to count the phonemes on his or her fingers.

STEP 3 BLEND THE SOUNDS
The little alien Phoneme Fred is useful here. Poor Phoneme Fred can only speak in separate phonemes – *c / a / t* – and your child will be able to help him to blend these into a spoken word.

STEP 4 SPLIT THE WORD INTO SOUNDS
Hearing the phonemes, and saying them in quick succession, prepares children for spelling.

STEP 5 READ THE WORD
Your child is taught how to read the word phoneme by phoneme, always going from left to right.

STEP 6 SPELL THE WORD
This is a writing activity, in which your child will learn how to turn the phonemes into graphemes, or written letters. Ask your child to read his or her writing back to you.

Some children take time to learn how to write. Don't spend too long on this step, and don't worry if your child's spelling is not developing as quickly as his or her reading.

Phoneme Fred

Step 4: Split the word into sounds

- Say *flash*, and ask your child to say the word as Phoneme Fred would say it.

- Repeat this for words that rhyme with *flash*.

Step 5: Read the word

> Words containing graphemes which have not yet been taught are printed in blue.

Fla**sh** went the lightning, cra**sh** went the thunder and spla**sh** went the rain.

fla**sh**	me**sh**	di**sh**	po**sh**	ru**sh**
cra**sh**	fle**sh**	fi**sh**	splo**sh**	**th**ru**sh**
a**sh**	fre**sh**	wi**sh**	slo**sh**	hu**sh**

- Read the sentence at the top of the box with your child.

- Point to the word *flash*. Say: Read this word so that Phoneme Fred can understand it.

- When your child has said the sounds *f-l-a-sh*, ask: What is the word?

- Choose other words for your child to read, column by column and then at random.

> If the word begins with two or three separately pronounced consonants, let your child practise saying these phonemes quickly:
> *f-l fl   s-p-l spl*

Step 6: Spell the word

- Choose words from the box, column by column and then at random. Say:

  Read this word so that Phoneme Fred can understand it. Write the word.

> Make sure your child starts each letter in the correct place. (See Book 1.)

- Ask your child to underline each grapheme:

  <u>f</u> <u>l</u> <u>a</u> <u>sh</u>

> Don't forget: Read all the letter sounds with your child every day. (See the alphabet strip at the top of this page and page 4.)

Unit 2: Words that rhyme with *hand*

Step 1: Find the rhyming words

◆ Help your child to think of words that rhyme with **hand**.
Say the words together: sand band land grand stand brand and bland

◆ Say this rhyming sentence:

Hand in hand we land on the sand.

Step 2: Find the sounds

◆ Play Phoneme Fingers. Say each of the **and** words
with your child, counting the phonemes on your fingers:

a-n-d   (3 phonemes)

h-a-n-d s-a-n-d b-a-n-d l-a-n-d   (4 phonemes)

g-r-a-n-d s-t-a-n-d b-r-a-n-d b-l-a-n-d   (5 phonemes)

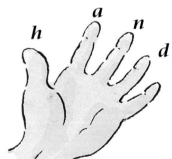

See how quickly your child can
count the phonemes on her fingers.

Step 3: Blend the sounds

◆ Say:

Phoneme Fred is trying to say this word: **h-a-n-d**
What is the word?

◆ Repeat this for words that rhyme with **hand**.

Step 4: Split the word into sounds

▶ Say **hand**, and ask your child to say the word as Phoneme Fred would say it.

▶ Repeat this for words that rhyme with **hand**.

Step 5: Read the word

Hand in hand we land on the sand.		
hand	bend	fond
brand	send	bond
and	end	pond

▶ Read the sentence at the top of the box with your child.

> Point to each grapheme in turn, emphasising the left-to-right movement.

▶ Point to the word **hand**. Say: Read this word so that Phoneme Fred can understand it.

▶ When your child has said the sounds **h-a-n-d**, ask: What is the word?

▶ Choose other words for your child to read, column by column and then at random.

> If the word begins with two separately pronounced consonants, let your child practise saying these phonemes quickly:
> **b-r br**

Step 6: Spell the word

▶ Choose words from the box, column by column and then at random. Say:

> Read this word so that Phoneme Fred can understand it.
> Write the word.

▶ Ask your child to underline each grapheme:

<u>h</u> <u>a</u> <u>n</u> <u>d</u>

> Don't forget: Read all the letter sounds with your child every day. (See the alphabet strip at the top of this page and page 6.)

sh and *nd*

◆ Ask your child to read each set of words, emphasising the vowel sound.

fla<u>sh</u>	fle<u>sh</u>	hand		
ba<u>sh</u>		band	bend	bond
da<u>sh</u>	di<u>sh</u>	stand		
ha<u>sh</u>	hu<u>sh</u>	grand		
cla<u>sh</u>		strand		
spla<u>sh</u>	splo<u>sh</u>	sand	send	
ra<u>sh</u>	ru<u>sh</u>	and	end	
<u>th</u>ra<u>sh</u>	<u>th</u>ru<u>sh</u>	land	lend	
ma<u>sh</u>	me<u>sh</u>	brand		
ca<u>sh</u>		bland	blend	

Tell your child that some of the words learned so far have been mixed up.

Ask your child to read each word.

di<u>sh</u>	band	bend
stand	cla<u>sh</u>	grand
spla<u>sh</u>	splo<u>sh</u>	strand
ra<u>sh</u>	end	ma<u>sh</u>
ba<u>sh</u>	hand	da<u>sh</u>
me<u>sh</u>	ru<u>sh</u>	sand
send	land	lend
fla<u>sh</u>	fle<u>sh</u>	brand
bond	ha<u>sh</u>	hu<u>sh</u>
<u>th</u>ra<u>sh</u>	<u>th</u>ru<u>sh</u>	and
ca<u>sh</u>	bland	blend

Unit 3: Words that rhyme with *bell* a b c

Step 1: Find the rhyming words

◆ Help your child to think of words that rhyme with *bell*. Say the words together:

> *sell   shell   well   swell   tell   spell   smell   yell   fell*

◆ Say this rhyming sentence:

> Ding dong bell, Pussy's in the well.

Step 2: Find the sounds

> Remember that *ll* and *sh* are single phonemes, each represented by two letters.

◆ Play Phoneme Fingers. Say each of the *ell* words with your child, counting the phonemes on your fingers:

> *b-e-ll   s-e-ll   sh-e-ll   w-e-ll   t-e-ll   y-e-ll   f-e-ll*   (3 phonemes)

> *s-w-e-ll   s-p-e-ll   s-m-e-ll*   (4 phonemes)

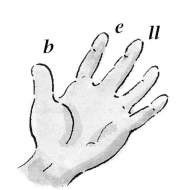

Step 3: Blend the sounds

◆ Say:

> Phoneme Fred is trying to say this word: *b-e-ll*
> What is the word?

◆ Repeat this for words that rhyme with *bell*.

Step 4: Split the word into sounds

- Say **bell**, and ask your child to say the word as Phoneme Fred would say it.

- Repeat this for words that rhyme with **bell**.

Step 5: Read the word

Ding dong be**ll**, Pussy's in the we**ll**.

be**ll**	sha**ll**	wi**ll**	bu**ll**	do**ll**
spe**ll**	ma**ll**	fi**ll**	fu**ll**	
she**ll**		ki**ll**	pu**ll**	

- Read the sentence at the top of the box with your child.

- Point to the word **bell**. Say: Read this word so that Phoneme Fred can understand it.

- When your child has said the sounds **b-e-ll**, ask: What is the word?

- Choose other words for your child to read, column by column and then at random.

> If the word begins with two separately pronounced consonants, let your child practise saying these phonemes quickly:
> **s-p sp**

Step 6: Spell the word

- Choose words from the box, column by column and then at random. Say:

  Read this word so that Phoneme Fred can understand it.
  Write the word.

- Ask your child to underline each grapheme:

  b e ll

> Don't forget: Read all the letter sounds with your child every day. (See the alphabet strip at the top of this page and page 10.)

11

Unit 4: Words that rhyme with *dress*

Step 1: Find the rhyming words

◆ Help your child to think of words that rhyme with **dress**.
Say the words together: | mess less guess bless press cress chess stress

◆ Say this rhyming sentence:

Guess who made the mess on my dress.

Step 2: Find the sounds

> Remember that **ss** and **ch** are single phonemes, represented by two letters.

◆ Play Phoneme Fingers. Say each of the **ess** words with your child, counting the phonemes on your fingers:

m-e-ss l-e-ss gu-e-ss ch-e-ss   (3 phonemes)

d-r-e-ss b-l-e-ss p-r-e-ss c-r-e-ss   (4 phonemes)

s-t-r-e-ss   (5 phonemes)

Step 3: Blend the sounds

◆ Say:

Phoneme Fred is trying to say this word: *d-r-e-ss*
What is the word?

◆ Repeat this for words that rhyme with **dress**.

Step 4: Split the word into sounds

▶ Say *dress*, and ask your child to say the word as Phoneme Fred would say it.

▶ Repeat this for words that rhyme with *dress*.

Step 5: Read the word

> The word *guess* contains a silent letter (*u*). Explain to your child that this letter is not pronounced.

Gu**e**ss who made the **mess** on my **dress**.

dress	lass	miss	moss	fuss
stress	mass	hiss	toss	
press	ass	kiss	cross	

▶ Read the sentence at the top of the box with your child.

▶ Point to the word *dress*. Say: Read this word so that Phoneme Fred can understand it.

▶ When your child has said the sounds *d-r-e-ss*, ask: What is the word?

▶ Choose other words for your child to read, column by column and then at random.

> If the word begins with two or three separately pronounced consonants, let your child practise saying these phonemes quickly:
> *d-r   dr   s-t-r   str*

Step 6: Spell the word

▶ Choose words from the box, column by column and then at random. Say:

> Read this word so that Phoneme Fred can understand it.
> Write the word.

▶ Ask your child to underline each grapheme:

d r e ss

> Don't forget: Read all the letter sounds with your child every day. (See the alphabet strip at the top of this page and page 12.)

13

ll and ss

◆ Ask your child to read each set of words, emphasising the vowel sound.

bell	bull	dress		
sell	sill	guess		
swell	swill	bless	bliss	
shell	shall	less	loss	lass
well	will	cress	cross	
tell	till	chess		
smell		mess	miss	mass
fell	full	stress		
yell		press		
spell	spill			

Tell your child that some of the words learned so far have been mixed up.

Ask your child to read each word.

swill	bless	bliss
cross	tell	till
mess	shell	stress
bull	sell	smell
yell	loss	will
lass	swell	guess
fell	press	shall
spell	spill	full
mass	cress	bell
sill	chess	dress
well	miss	less

Unit 5: Words that rhyme with *spring*

Step 1: Find the rhyming word

◆ Help your child to think of words that rhyme with *spring*. Say the words together:

> sing cling fling sling ring zing ping king thing wing string bring sting swing

◆ Say this rhyming sentence:

> Bring me a thing with a string and a spring.

> The consonants *ng* form a single phoneme. Exaggerate this nasal sound when you say the words.

Step 2: Find the sounds

> Remember that *th* is a single phoneme represented by two letters.

◆ Play Phoneme Fingers. Say each of the *ing* words with your child, counting the phonemes on your fingers:

> s-i-ng r-i-ng z-i-ng p-i-ng k-i-ng th-i-ng w-i-ng   (3 phonemes)

> c-l-i-ng f-l-i-ng s-l-i-ng b-r-i-ng s-t-i-ng s-w-i-ng   (4 phonemes)

> s-p-r-i-ng s-t-r-i-ng   (5 phonemes)

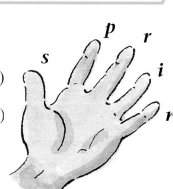

Step 3: Blend the sounds

◆ Say:

> Phoneme Fred is trying to say this word: *s-p-r-i-ng*
> What is the word?

◆ Repeat this for words that rhyme with *spring*.

Step 4: Split the word into sounds

Say **spring**, and ask your child to say the word as Phoneme Fred would say it.

Repeat this for words that rhyme with **spring**.

Step 5: Read the word

Bring <u>me</u> a <u>thing</u> wi<u>th</u> a stri<u>ng</u> and a spri<u>ng</u>.

spri<u>ng</u>	ba<u>ng</u>	spru<u>ng</u>	lo<u>ng</u>
cli<u>ng</u>	ra<u>ng</u>	stu<u>ng</u>	so<u>ng</u>
stri<u>ng</u>	ha<u>ng</u>	lu<u>ng</u>	go<u>ng</u>

• Read the sentence at the top of the box with your child.

• Point to the word **spring**. Say: Read this word so that Phoneme Fred can understand it.

• When your child has said the sounds **s-p-r-i-ng**, ask: What is the word?

• Choose other words for your child to read, column by column and then at random.

If the word begins with two or three separately pronounced consonants, let your child practise saying these phonemes quickly:
c-l   cl   s-p-r   spr

Step 6: Spell the word

• Choose words from the box, column by column and then at random. Say:

Read this word so that Phoneme Fred can understand it.
Write the word.

• Ask your child to underline each grapheme:

s p r i ng

Don't forget: Read all the letter sounds with your child every day. (See the alphabet strip at the top of this page and page 16.)

Unit 6: Words that rhyme with *clock* a b c

Step 1: Find the rhyming words

◆ Help your child to think of words that rhyme with *clock*. Say the words together:

> cock flock mock smock dock block lock rock knock sock shock stock

◆ Say this rhyming sentence:

> Hickory, dickory, dock, the mouse ran up the clock.

Step 2: Find the sounds

Remember that **sh** and **ck** are single phonemes, each represented by two letters.

◆ Play Phoneme Fingers. Say each of the *ock* words with your child, counting the phonemes on your fingers:

> c-o-ck m-o-ck d-o-ck l-o-ck r-o-ck kn-o-ck s-o-ck sh-o-ck   (3 phonemes)

> c-l-o-ck f-l-o-ck s-m-o-ck b-l-o-ck s-t-o-ck   (4 phonemes)

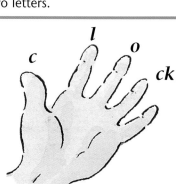

Step 3: Blend the sounds

◆ Say:

> Phoneme Fred is trying to say this word: *c-l-o-ck*
> What is the word?

◆ Repeat this for words that rhyme with *clock*.

Step 4: Split the word into sounds

- Say *clock*, and ask your child to say the word as Phoneme Fred would say it.

- Repeat this for words that rhyme with *clock*.

> The word *knock* contains a silent letter (the first *k*). Explain to your child that this letter is not pronounced.

Step 5: Read the word

Hickory, dickory, **do<u>ck</u>**, the mouse **ran up** the **clo<u>ck</u>**.

clo<u>ck</u>	si<u>ck</u>	du<u>ck</u>	sa<u>ck</u>	ne<u>ck</u>
k no<u>ck</u>	pi<u>ck</u>	clu<u>ck</u>	tra<u>ck</u>	de<u>ck</u>
<u>sh</u>o<u>ck</u>	ti<u>ck</u>	stu<u>ck</u>	ba<u>ck</u>	spe<u>ck</u>

- Read the sentence at the top of the box with your child.

- Point to the word *clock*. Say: Read this word so that Phoneme Fred can understand it.

- When your child has said the sounds *c-l-o-ck*, ask: What is the word?

- Choose other words for your child to read, column by column and then at random.

> If the word begins with two separately pronounced consonants, let your child practise saying these phonemes quickly:
> *c-l   cl*

Step 6: Spell the word

- Choose words from the box, column by column and then at random. Say:

  Read this word so that Phoneme Fred can understand it.
  Write the word.

- Ask your child to underline each grapheme:

  c l o ck

> Don't forget: Read all the letter sounds with your child every day. (See the alphabet strip at the top of this page and page 18.)

ng and ck

◆ Ask your child to read each set of words, emphasising the vowel sound.

spri**ng**		clo**ck**	cl**ick**	clu**ck**
swi**ng**		do**ck**	du**ck**	de**ck**
wi**ng**		lo**ck**	li**ck**	lu**ck**
bri**ng**		kno**ck**	kna**ck**	
thi**ng**		ro**ck**	ra**ck**	
ri**ng**	ra**ng**	sto**ck**	sta**ck**	sti**ck**
sti**ng**	stu**ng**	flo**ck**	fle**ck**	fli**ck**
sli**ng**	sla**ng**	mo**ck**	mu**ck**	
si**ng**	su**ng**	co**ck**		
ki**ng**		so**ck**	si**ck**	su**ck**

Tell your child that some of the words learned so far have been mixed up.

Ask your child to read each word.

stung	thing	duck
cock	fleck	sing
dock	bring	sick
ring	sock	flock
stock	knack	lock
sling	rock	sung
stack	stick	knock
wing	king	muck
rang	deck	flick
mock	click	clock
spring	lick	sting
rack	slang	luck
cluck	swing	suck

Step 1: Find the rhyming words

◆ Help your child to think of words that rhyme with **jump**.

Say the words together: *pump stump bump dump lump thump slump*

◆ Say this rhyming sentence:

  Bump, bump, bump, you made me jump.

> Make sure your child runs the final **m** and **p** together, although they are two separate phonemes.

Step 2: Find the sounds

◆ Play Phoneme Fingers. Say each of the **ump** words with your child, counting the phonemes on your fingers:

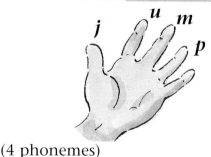

  j-u-m-p p-u-m-p b-u-m-p d-u-m-p l-u-m-p th-u-m-p (4 phonemes)

  s-t-u-m-p s-l-u-m-p   (5 phonemes)

> Remember that **th** is one phoneme represented by two letters.

Step 3: Blend the sounds

◆ Say:

  Phoneme Fred is trying to say this word: **j-u-m-p**
  What is the word?

◆ Repeat this for words that rhyme with **jump**.

Step 4: Split the word into sounds

- Say **jump**, and ask your child to say the word as Phoneme Fred would say it.

- Repeat this for words that rhyme with **jump**.

Step 5: Read the word

Bump, bump, bump, you made me jump.

jump	lamp	romp	limp
stump	stamp	<u>ch</u>omp	<u>ch</u>imp
pump	ramp	pomp	<u>sh</u>rimp

- Read the sentence at the top of the box with your child.

- Point to the word **jump**. Say: Read this word so that Phoneme Fred can understand it.

- When your child has said the sounds **j-u-m-p**, ask: What is the word?

- Choose other words for your child to read, column by column and then at random.

> If the word begins with two separately pronounced consonants, let your child practise saying these phonemes quickly: *s-t st*

Step 6: Spell the word

- Choose words from the box, column by column and then at random. Say:

  Read this word so that Phoneme Fred can understand it.
  Write the word.

- Ask your child to underline each grapheme:

  j <u>u</u> m p

> Don't forget: Read all the letter sounds with your child every day. (See the alphabet strip at the top of this page and page 22.)

Unit 8: Words that rhyme with *book*

Step 1: Find the rhyming words

◆ Help your child to think of words that rhyme with **book**.

Say the words together: cook hook look rook brook crook shook took

◆ Say this rhyming sentence:

Look at a book when you try to cook.

Step 2: Find the sounds

Remember that *sh* and *oo* are single phonemes, each represented by two letters.

◆ Play Phoneme Fingers. Say each of the **ook** words with your child, counting the phonemes on your fingers:

b-oo-k c-oo-k h-oo-k l-oo-k r-oo-k sh-oo-k t-oo-k   (3 phonemes)

b-r-oo-k c-r-oo-k   (4 phonemes)

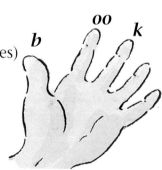

Step 3: Blend the sounds

◆ Say:

Phoneme Fred is trying to say this word: *b-oo-k*
What is the word?

◆ Repeat this for words that rhyme with **book**.

24

Step 4: Split the word into sounds

- Say **book**, and ask your child to say the word as Phoneme Fred would say it.

- Repeat this for words that rhyme with **book**.

> Tell your child that the **oo** in the word **look** is a pair of eyes! Write **oo**, and draw a bridge to make a picture of a pair of glasses.

Step 5: Read the word

Look at a b<u>oo</u>k <u>when</u> you try to c<u>oo</u>k.

b<u>oo</u>k	t<u>oo</u>k	sh<u>oo</u>k
br<u>oo</u>k	cr<u>oo</u>k	r<u>oo</u>k
h<u>oo</u>k	c<u>oo</u>k	l<u>oo</u>k

- Read the sentence at the top of the box with your child.

- Point to the word **book**. Say: Read this word so that Phoneme Fred can understand it.

- When your child has said the sounds **b-oo-k**, ask: What is the word?

- Choose other words for your child to read.

> If the word begins with two separately pronounced consonants, let your child practise saying these phonemes quickly:
> **b-r br   c-r cr**

Step 6: Spell the word

- Choose words from the box. Say:

  Read this word so that Phoneme Fred can understand it. Write the word.

- Ask your child to underline each grapheme:

  <u>b</u> <u>oo</u> <u>k</u>

> Don't forget: Read all the letter sounds with your child every day. (See the alphabet strip at the top of this page and page 24.)

mp and ook

◆ Ask your child to read each set of words, emphasising the vowel sound.

jump			b<u>oo</u>k
pump			br<u>oo</u>k
stump	stamp		cr<u>oo</u>k
plump			<u>sh</u><u>oo</u>k
lump	lamp	limp	t<u>oo</u>k
clump	clamp		c<u>oo</u>k
dump	damp		h<u>oo</u>k
hump			l<u>oo</u>k
<u>th</u>ump			r<u>oo</u>k
bump			

Tell your child that some of the words learned so far have been mixed up.

Ask your child to read each word.

stump	damp	cr<u>oo</u>k
lamp	clump	hump
br<u>oo</u>k	bump	c<u>oo</u>k
jump	clamp	t<u>oo</u>k
limp	<u>sh</u><u>oo</u>k	<u>th</u>ump
stamp	lump	b<u>oo</u>k
h<u>oo</u>k	plump	l<u>oo</u>k
dump	r<u>oo</u>k	pump

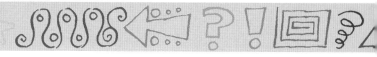
Read the following poems with your child.

Mud

I love mud.
Thick, icky mud.

Thick lumps of mud.
Thick clumps of mud.

I jump in it.
I slump in it.
I slop in it.
I flop in it.

Words containing graphemes which have not yet been taught are printed in blue. Help your child to read these words by looking at any graphemes which are familiar, and by predicting the words from his or her knowledge of the poem. Teach your child to read *of, I, the* and *my*.

I dig my fingers in,
and press my hands
into the thick, icky mud.

I mix the mud and I mash the mud.

Messing and pressing,
pressing and messing.

I love mud.
Thick, icky mud.

Kite on a string

Look at my kite on a string!

Look, as I fling the string
to make it spin and spring!

Look at my kite on a string!

Look, as it drops and flops,
and bumps and thumps on the grass.

Look at my kite on a string!

My best dress

Look at the mess on my dress!

Look at the mess on my best dress!

Look at the mess on my best
black and red dress!

Look at the mess on my best
black and red frilly dress!

Look at the mess on my best
black and red frilly dress
with spots on!

Look at the mess on my dress!

What shall I tell my mum?

Sand and shells

See the water splash across the sand.

See the water crash across the slippery rocks.

See the children dash as the waves rush
towards their feet.

See the children pick their way between the waves.

See the children kick the shiny, wet pebbles.

See the children run when it's time
for sandwiches and hot soup!

Hear the shrill sound of their voices
as they yell when their wellingtons fill with water.

Hear them at the end of the day,
searching for shells on the path.